The dream

I had a dream, a bad dream too.
I dreamed that I was at the zoo.
A sheep, a yak, two chimps, a seal,
Sat round on seats to eat a meal.

One seat was free, and I could see
That this one seat was free for me.
'Oh good,' the sheep said with a bleat,
'I think we can begin to eat.'

The seals had fish, the sheep had beet.
The chimps had beans and peas with meat.
The yak had heaps of moss for tea.
There was a dish of eels for me.

'A feast of eels!' I yelled. 'What cheek!
I had eels every day last week.'
And then I yelled out in my dream,
'I wanted snails with salad cream!'

The most precious thing

Once upon a time, there lived a king
   and a queen.
The king and queen were old and
   they had no children.

5

'I feel I will soon be too old to
   be the king,' said the king.
'And I will be too old to be queen,'
   said the queen, 'but what can we do?'

6

'We need someone to do the job for
    us,' said the king.
'We need to teach someone what to
    do,' said the queen, 'but who?'

7

The next day a bill was put up.
It said, 'We seek a new king or queen.
If you can bring the most precious
    thing to us, the job is yours.'

8

The next day, people came from all
  over the land.
They all had precious things with them.
Some had silver, some had gold.

The king looked at the treasure and
shook his head.
'You are all fools,' he said. 'Gold and
silver are not the most precious things.'

The king said, 'If you think treasure
is precious, you will be weak.
You will deal with people who will
cheat you.'

'Didn't one of you bring the most precious
    thing?' asked the queen.
Just then a girl came up.
She had a little box in her hand.

'I am not rich and I do not bring treasure,'
said the girl, 'but this is precious.'
She gave the box to the queen and
the queen looked inside.

The box was full of seeds.
'Seeds are precious,' said the girl.
'We can't do without them and
    they are free to everyone.
Even a king can do without gold.'

The queen took the girl by the hand.
'You shall be the new queen,' she said.
'For you can see what it means to
    be a king or a queen.'

Snail trails

Dad came in my room.
I could tell he was mad.
He had on the look that
    he gets when I'm bad.

But why he was cross I just
    couldn't think.
Then Dad asked me why there
    were snails in the sink.

I ran down with Dad to
    look at my snails.
All over the kitchen were
    six silver trails.

Dad gave me a mop and
    he gave me a pail.
To clean up the mess and
    get rid of each snail.

'Next time, think,' said my dad.
'Get it plain in your brain.
Snails are not pets, so
    don't do it again.'

I did want a pet, like
a dog or a cat.
But dad said I couldn't,
'No pets, and that's that.'

21

'No pets! Well, we'll see.'
I went out in the rain,
and found a fat slug by
the back of the drain.

The little spook

I met a spook out in the hall,
It gave a wail, and made a hoot.
I didn't feel afraid at all.
It went 'woo-woo' and 'root-toot-toot'.

The spook then said, 'It seems to me
That I don't fill you full of dread.'
'You're such a little spook, you see,
I'm not afraid of you,' I said.